WIN WITHIN

- - - - - - -

A Journal That Empowers the Mind

Shana M. Fleming

Win Within
A Journal That Empowers the Mind
Copyright 2023
Shana M. Fleming

Publisher: Nissi Sing, LLC

Editor: Nissi Singh

WHERE TO PURCHASE WIN WITHIN? **AMAZON.COM**

INSPIRATION

Thank you to the Beautiful souls incarcerated at Coffee Correctional Facility! It was you that inspired this journal. I am forever grateful for the opportunity to serve.

Special Thanks

I want to express gratitude towards my family and friends that exemplify love and support through their actions. God, with you ALL things are possible!

AND THE WINNER IS …

_____!
Your Name

This journal was created just for you. Yes, YOU! It has a one day at a time approach to transform your thoughts. Remember to be kind to yourself and trust the process. Each day offers a new beginning FULL of possibilities. I encourage you to choose Today, this Moment, this Time; the choice is yours. Learn to develop the mind of a champion through Self Discovery, Self-Respect, and ultimately, Self-Love.

With Excitement,
S. M. Fleming
Shana M. Fleming

FEELINGS COLLAGE

cheerful   ANGRY   arrogant   Bashful

bored   CAUTIOUS   Confident   *confused*

PROUD   curious   Disappointed   Free

SUSPICIOUS   disgusted   **ecstatic**

Inspired   ENVIOUS   **excited**   Frustrated

determined   Guilty   *HAPPY*   passionate

Hurt   *satisfied*   **joyful**   LONELY   pride

energized   *nervous*   **optimistic**   Hopeful

sad   **SATISFIED**   scared   Shocked

PLAYFUL   Stubborn   *surprised*   Peaceful

Sympathetic   UNDECIDED   **withdrawn**   accepted

DEFINITIONS

Win Within

The process of learning who you are in an effort to create a solid foundation for endless possibilities.

Feelings Statement

Describes the current state of mind, functioning, or thought processes.

Today, I choose to Win Within because ...

_____

_____

_____

_____

_____

_____

_____

_____

_____

_____

_____

Who am I?

It is important to have inner peace because...

_____

_____

_____

_____

_____

_____

_____

_____

_____

_____

I am Most Happy When...

_____

_____

_____

_____

_____

_____

_____

_____

_____

_____

I Feel Most Loved When ...

TRUE or *FALSE* (Circle)

I Am a Leader (*Provide 3 Examples*)

1._____

_____

2._____

_____

3._____

_____

On a Scale From 1------------------------10

Least   *Greatest*

How Confident Am I?
(Provide an Example)

_____

_____

_____

_____

_____

_____

_____

_____

_____

How Am I Working Towards Becoming A Better Person?

Describe or Draw Yourself

N O W	F U T U R E

Write a Letter to Your Younger Self

_____

_____

_____

_____

_____

_____

_____

_____

_____

_____

List 5 Things That Motivate You

1._____

2._____

3._____

4._____

5._____

Free Space

This is Your Opportunity to Be Creative in Expressing YOU ...

Y E S   or   *N O*   (Circle)

Is There Anything from My Childhood that Impacts Me?

Explanation ...

_____

_____

_____

_____

_____

_____

_____

_____

_____

_____

How Does My Family View Me?

Does It Match How I View Me?

_____

_____

_____

_____

_____

_____

_____

_____

_____

_____

Share A Favorite Childhood Memory

What Does the Word "Love" Mean?

TRUE or *FALSE* (Circle)

I Am Worthy of Love?

Explain...

When I Feel Like Giving Up,

Where Do I Find Strength to Continue

The Fight?

_____

_____

_____

_____

_____

_____

_____

_____

_____

List 3 Ways You Show Strength

>

>

>

Do I Forgive Those That Have Done Me Wrong?
(Explain)

Free Space

This is Your Opportunity to Be Creative in Expressing YOU

Today, I Choose to Be...
(Refer to Feelings Collage page 6)

Describe ...

_____

_____

_____

_____

_____

_____

_____

_____

_____

_____

My Friends Describe Me As...

_____

_____

_____

_____

_____

_____

_____

_____

_____

_____

List as Many Positive Characteristics About Yourself

TRUE or *FALSE* (Circle)

I Have What It Takes to Conquer My Fears!

Explain...

Being _____ has impacted my life because...

(Fill in blank with a word that describes you)

TRUE   or   *FALSE*   (Circle)

I Deserve a Second Chance (Explain)

What Advice Would You Give Someone?

I Forgive Myself For Past Mistakes Because...

Circle Traits That Align With Who You Are:

Honest

Kind

Faithful

Genuine

Positive

Leader

Patient

Self-Control

Joyful

I Am Worthy of Love Because...
(List Reasons)

- _____

- _____

- _____

- _____

- _____

- _____

- _____

- _____

- _____

- _____

Y E S   or   *N O*   (Circle)

I Have Talents and Gifts.

(Explain)

_____

_____

_____

_____

_____

_____

_____

_____

_____

Free Space

This is Your Opportunity to Be Creative in Expressing YOU ...

Control Chart

Things in My Control	Things out of My Control

How Do I Adapt to Change?

_____

_____

_____

_____

_____

_____

_____

_____

_____

What is Respect?

I Show Respect to Others By:

Provide 3 Examples

1._____

_____

2._____

_____

3._____

_____

What Happens When I Feel Disrespected?

Today, I Feel

(Draw a Picture of Feelings Statement)
Refer to Feelings Collage page 6

Feelings Statement

I tend to feel _____ most of the time

because_____

_____

TRUE or *FALSE* (Circle)

I Know Who I Am

Explain ...

_____

_____

_____

_____

_____

_____

_____

_____

_____

_____

Y E S   or   *N O*   (Circle)

Do I Allow Others to Influence Me?

Describe

List 3 Ways I Have Influenced Others:

1._____

_____

2._____

_____

3._____

_____

What Gives Me Hope?

Feelings Statement

Today was a good day because _____

_____;

Tomorrow, I can make it a better day by_____

_____

I Am So Proud of You!

Continue to build strength in getting to know who you are. With each day you gain a stronger sense of self, which embodies the mindset of a winner!

Today, I Choose to Win Within By ...

_____

_____

_____

_____

_____

_____

_____

_____

_____

_____

Today, I Choose to Win Within By ...

_____

_____

_____

_____

_____

_____

_____

_____

_____

_____

Today, I Choose to Win Within By ...

_____

_____

_____

_____

_____

_____

_____

_____

_____

_____

Today, I Choose to Win Within By …

_____

_____

_____

_____

_____

_____

_____

_____

_____

_____

Today, I Choose to Win Within By ...

_____

_____

_____

_____

_____

_____

_____

_____

_____

_____

Today, I Choose to Win Within By ...

_____

_____

_____

_____

_____

_____

_____

_____

_____

_____

Today, I Choose to Win Within By …

_____

_____

_____

_____

_____

_____

_____

_____

_____

_____

WOW, Look at you!

Take a Deep Breath; Exhale, as you look within, CONTINUE TO WIN!

The next pages are yours to Explore!
Keep writing, the choice and topics are
YOURS!

CONTINUE TO WIN!

_____

_____

_____

_____

_____

_____

_____

_____

_____

_____

CONTINUE TO WIN!

_____

_____

_____

_____

_____

_____

_____

_____

_____

_____

CONTINUE TO WIN!

_____

_____

_____

_____

_____

_____

_____

_____

_____

_____

CONTINUE TO WIN!

_____

_____

_____

_____

_____

_____

_____

_____

_____

_____

CONTINUE TO WIN!

_____

_____

_____

_____

_____

_____

_____

_____

_____

_____

CONTINUE TO WIN!

_____

_____

_____

_____

_____

_____

_____

_____

_____

_____

_____

CONTINUE TO WIN!

_____

_____

_____

_____

_____

_____

_____

_____

_____

_____

CONTINUE TO WIN!

_____

_____

_____

_____

_____

_____

_____

_____

_____

_____

_____

CONTINUE TO WIN!

CONTINUE TO WIN!

CONTINUE TO WIN!

_____

_____

_____

_____

_____

_____

_____

_____

_____

_____

CONTINUE TO WIN!

_____

_____

_____

_____

_____

_____

_____

_____

_____

CONTINUE TO WIN!

_____

_____

_____

_____

_____

_____

_____

_____

_____

_____

CONTINUE TO WIN!

_____

_____

_____

_____

_____

_____

_____

_____

_____

_____

CONTINUE TO WIN!

_____

_____

_____

_____

_____

_____

_____

_____

_____

_____

CONTINUE TO WIN!

_____

_____

_____

_____

_____

_____

_____

_____

_____

_____

CONTINUE TO WIN!

_____

_____

_____

_____

_____

_____

_____

_____

_____

_____

_____

CONTINUE TO WIN!

_____

_____

_____

_____

_____

_____

_____

_____

_____

_____

CONTINUE TO WIN!

_____

_____

_____

_____

_____

_____

_____

_____

_____

_____

CONTINUE TO WIN!

CONTINUE TO WIN!

CONTINUE TO WIN!

_____

_____

_____

_____

_____

_____

_____

_____

_____

_____

CONTINUE TO WIN!

_____

_____

_____

_____

_____

_____

_____

_____

_____

_____

CONTINUE TO WIN!

_____

_____

_____

_____

_____

_____

_____

_____

_____

_____

CONTINUE TO WIN!

_____

_____

_____

_____

_____

_____

_____

_____

_____

_____

CONTINUE TO WIN!

CONTINUE TO WIN!

_____

_____

_____

_____

_____

_____

_____

_____

_____

_____

CONTINUE TO WIN!

_____

_____

_____

_____

_____

_____

_____

_____

_____

_____

CONTINUE TO WIN!

_____

_____

_____

_____

_____

_____

_____

_____

_____

_____

CONTINUE TO WIN!

_____

_____

_____

_____

_____

_____

_____

_____

_____

_____

CONTINUE TO WIN!

CONTINUE TO WIN!

_____

_____

_____

_____

_____

_____

_____

_____

_____

_____

CONTINUE TO WIN!

_____

_____

_____

_____

_____

_____

_____

_____

_____

_____

CONTINUE TO WIN!

_____

_____

_____

_____

_____

_____

_____

_____

_____

_____

_____

CONTINUE TO WIN!

_____

_____

_____

_____

_____

_____

_____

_____

_____

_____

CONTINUE TO WIN!

_____

_____

_____

_____

_____

_____

_____

_____

_____

_____

CONTINUE TO WIN!

_____

_____

_____

_____

_____

_____

_____

_____

_____

_____

_____

CONTINUE TO WIN!

_____

_____

_____

_____

_____

_____

_____

_____

_____

_____

CONTINUE TO WIN!

_____

_____

_____

_____

_____

_____

_____

_____

_____

_____

CONTINUE TO WIN!

_____

_____

_____

_____

_____

_____

_____

_____

_____

_____

CONTINUE TO WIN!

_____

_____

_____

_____

_____

_____

_____

_____

_____

_____

_____

CONTINUE TO WIN!

_____

_____

_____

_____

_____

_____

_____

_____

_____

_____

_____

CONTINUE TO WIN!

_____

_____

_____

_____

_____

_____

_____

_____

_____

_____

_____

CONTINUE TO WIN!

_____

_____

_____

_____

_____

_____

_____

_____

_____

_____

CONTINUE TO WIN!

_____

_____

_____

_____

_____

_____

_____

_____

_____

_____

_____

CONTINUE TO WIN!

_____

_____

_____

_____

_____

_____

_____

_____

_____

_____

CONTINUE TO WIN!

_____

_____

_____

_____

_____

_____

_____

_____

_____

_____

_____

CONTINUE TO WIN!

_____

_____

_____

_____

_____

_____

_____

_____

_____

_____

_____

CONTINUE TO WIN!

_____

_____

_____

_____

_____

_____

_____

_____

_____

_____

CONTINUE TO WIN!

_____

_____

_____

_____

_____

_____

_____

_____

_____

_____

CONTINUE TO WIN!

_____

_____

_____

_____

_____

_____

_____

_____

_____

_____

_____

CONTINUE TO WIN!

_____

_____

_____

_____

_____

_____

_____

_____

_____

_____

CONTINUE TO WIN!

CONTINUE TO WIN!

CONTINUE TO WIN!

_____

_____

_____

_____

_____

_____

_____

_____

_____

CONTINUE TO WIN!

_____

_____

_____

_____

_____

_____

_____

_____

_____

_____

CONTINUE TO WIN!

_____

_____

_____

_____

_____

_____

_____

_____

_____

_____

CONTINUE TO WIN!

_____

_____

_____

_____

_____

_____

_____

_____

_____

_____

CONTINUE TO WIN!

_____

_____

_____

_____

_____

_____

_____

_____

_____

_____

_____

CONTINUE TO WIN!

_____

_____

_____

_____

_____

_____

_____

_____

_____

_____

_____

CONTINUE TO WIN!

_____

_____

_____

_____

_____

_____

_____

_____

_____

_____

CONTINUE TO WIN!

_____

_____

_____

_____

_____

_____

_____

_____

_____

CONTINUE TO WIN!

_____

_____

_____

_____

_____

_____

_____

_____

_____

_____

CONTINUE TO WIN!

CONTINUE TO WIN!

_____

_____

_____

_____

_____

_____

_____

_____

_____

_____

CONTINUE TO WIN!

CONTINUE TO WIN!

_____

_____

_____

_____

_____

_____

_____

_____

_____

_____

_____

CONTINUE TO WIN!

_____

_____

_____

_____

_____

_____

_____

_____

_____

_____

CONTINUE TO WIN!

_____

_____

_____

_____

_____

_____

_____

_____

_____

_____

CONTINUE TO WIN!

_____

_____

_____

_____

_____

_____

_____

_____

_____

_____

CONTINUE TO WIN!

_____

_____

_____

_____

_____

_____

_____

_____

_____

_____

CONTINUE TO WIN!

_____

_____

_____

_____

_____

_____

_____

_____

_____

_____

_____

CONTINUE TO WIN!

_____

_____

_____

_____

_____

_____

_____

_____

_____

_____

CONTINUE TO WIN!

_____

_____

_____

_____

_____

_____

_____

_____

_____

_____

CONTINUE TO WIN!

CONTINUE TO WIN!

_____

_____

_____

_____

_____

_____

_____

_____

_____

_____

_____

CONTINUE TO WIN!

_____

_____

_____

_____

_____

_____

_____

_____

_____

_____

CONTINUE TO WIN!

_____

_____

_____

_____

_____

_____

_____

_____

_____

_____

CONTINUE TO WIN!

_____

_____

_____

_____

_____

_____

_____

_____

_____

_____

_____

CONTINUE TO WIN!

_____

_____

_____

_____

_____

_____

_____

_____

_____

_____

CONTINUE TO WIN!

_____

_____

_____

_____

_____

_____

_____

_____

_____

_____

_____

CONTINUE TO WIN!

CONTINUE TO WIN!

CONTINUE TO WIN!

_____

_____

_____

_____

_____

_____

_____

_____

_____

_____

_____